RELAXING CLASSICS · A COOL COLLECTION OF PIANO SOLOS

RELAXING

GW01045634

CLASSICS

CHESTER MUSIC
part of the Music Sales Group
London/New York/Paris/Sydney/Copenhagen/Berlin/Madrid/Tokyo

Published by:
Chester Music Limited,
8/9 Frith Street, London W1D 3JB, England.

Exclusive Distributors:
Music Sales Limited,
Distribution Centre, Newmarket Road, Bury St Edmunds, Suffolk IP33 3YB, England.
Music Sales Pty Limited,
120 Rothschild Avenue, Rosebery, NSW 2018, Australia.

Order No. CH66847
ISBN 1-84449-067-X
This book © Copyright 2003 by Chester Music.

Compiled by Heather Ramage.

Dance Of The Blessed Spirits, Flow My Tears, Consolation No.3,
The Girl With The Flaxen Hair, Intermezzo, Piano Concerto No.2 (Adagio Sostenuto),
The Swan, Violin Concerto in E minor (Andante) and Vocalise arranged by Jerry Lanning.

Music processed by Note-orious Productions Limited.

Printed in the Malta by Interprint Limited.

ADAGIO IN G MINOR

Tomaso Albinoni

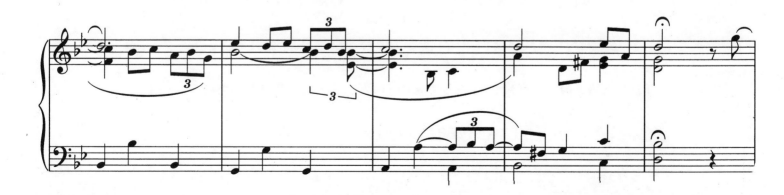

CLOSE COVER

Wim Mertens

CAVATINA

Stanley Myers

Slowly, with feeling

To ⊕ CODA

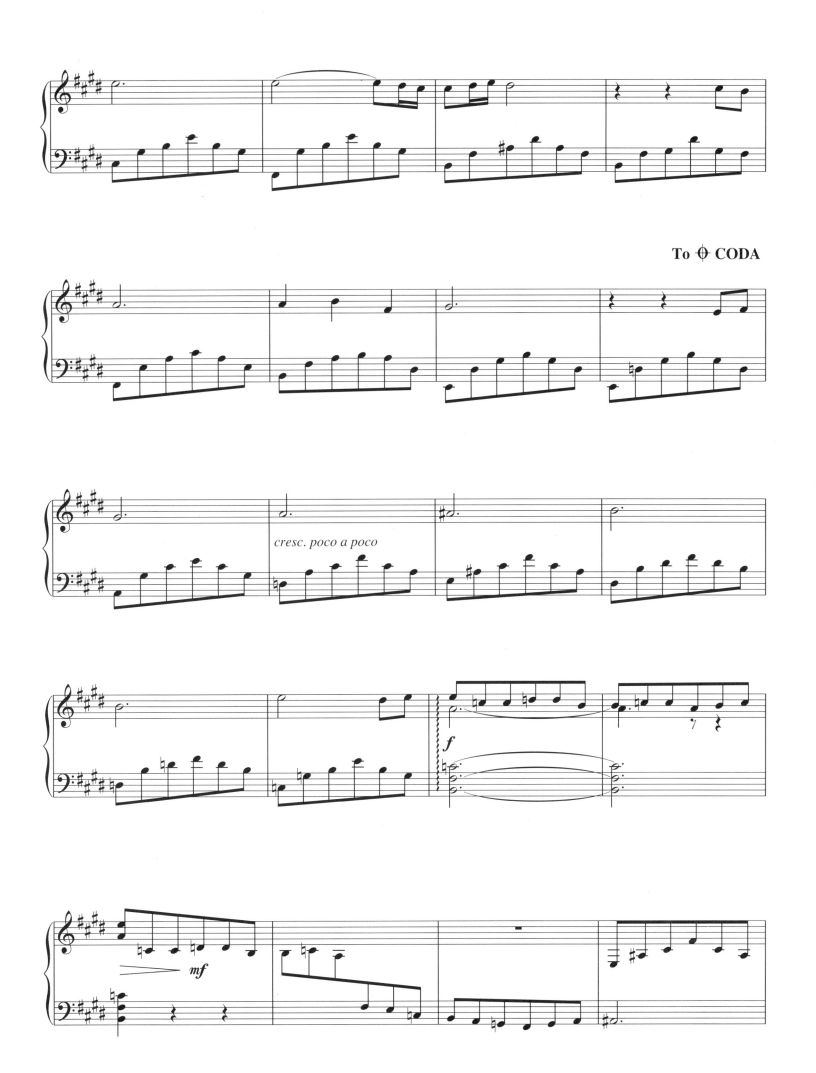

cresc. poco a poco

mf

cresc. poco a poco

mf

D.C. al ⊕ Coda

$\oplus$ **CODA**

poco rit.

molto rit.

DANCE OF THE BLESSED SPIRITS
(FROM 'ORFEO ED EURIDICE')

Christoph Willibald von Gluck

Lento ♩ = 84

ELEGIE

Jules Massenet

Lento, ma non troppo

FLOW MY TEARS

John Dowland

CONSOLATION NO.3

Franz Liszt

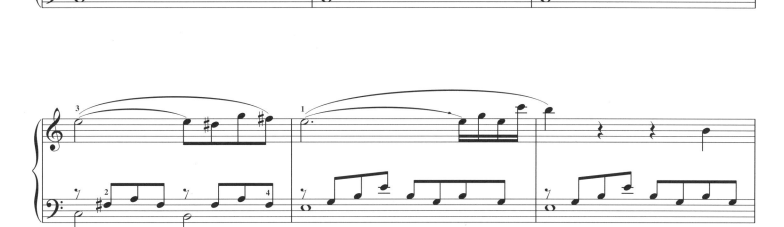

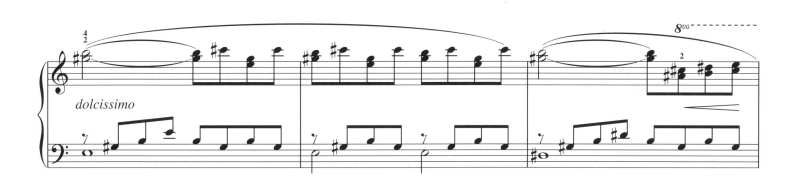

THE GIRL WITH THE FLAXEN HAIR

Claude Debussy

Very calm and sweetly expressive ♩ = 52

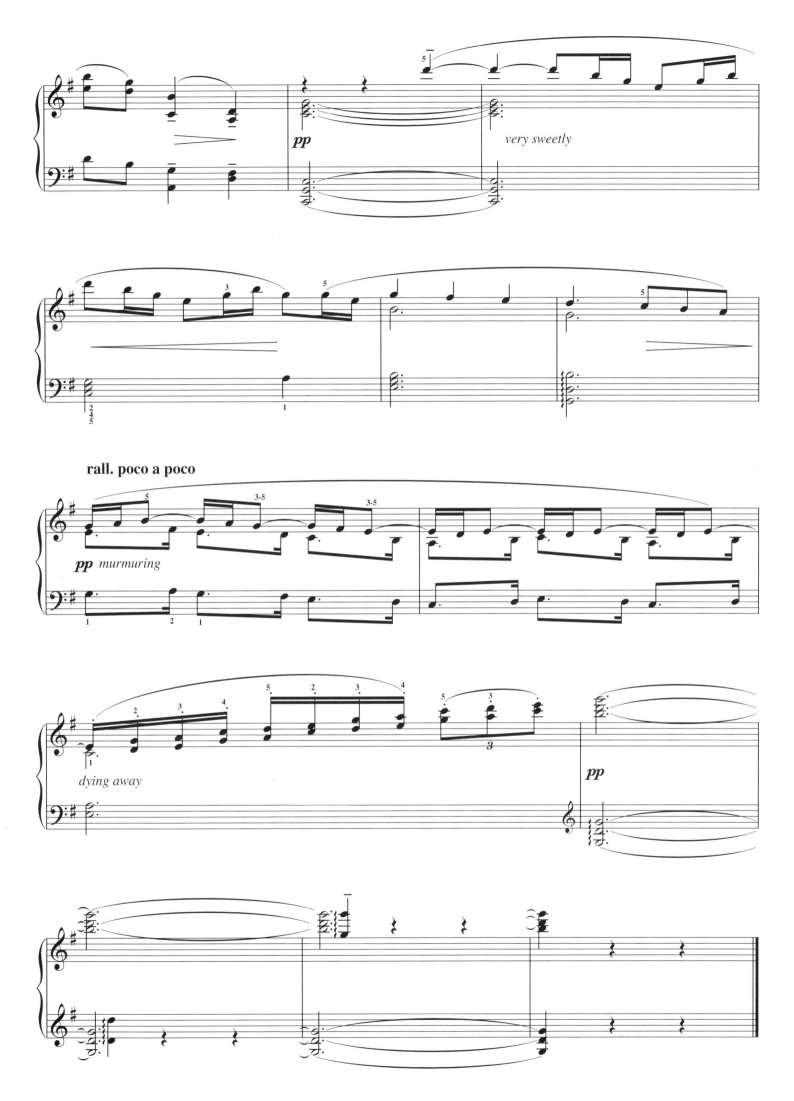

rall. poco a poco

very sweetly

pp *murmuring*

dying away

I KNOW THAT MY REDEEMER LIVETH
(FROM 'MESSIAH')

George Frideric Handel

Larghetto

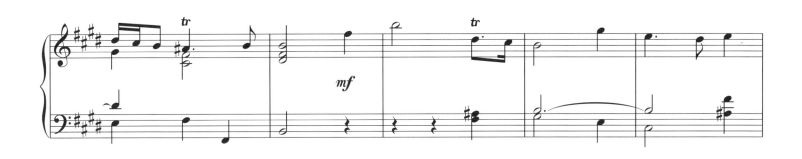

poco rit.   a tempo

INTERMEZZO
(FROM 'CARMEN')
Georges Bizet

Andantino quasi allegretto ♩ = 88

THE HOURS
(FROM THE FILM 'THE HOURS')
Phillip Glass

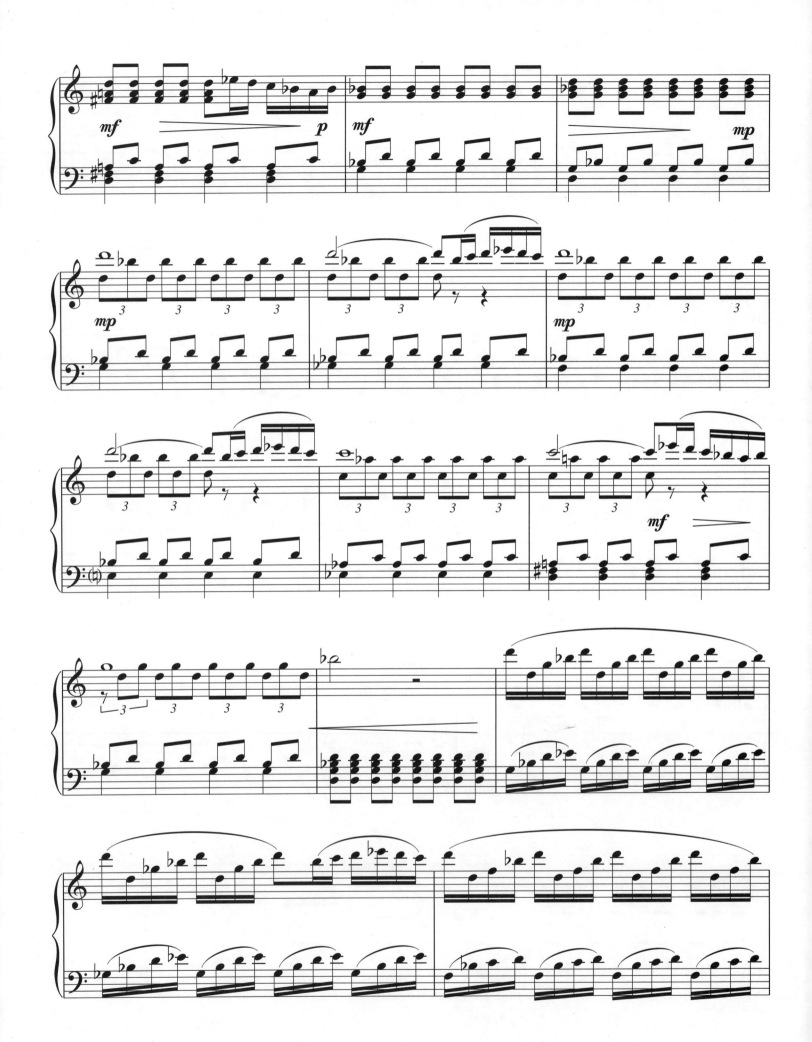

THE JOHN DUNBAR THEME
(FROM THE FILM 'DANCES WITH WOLVES')

John Barry

To Coda ⊕
(End opt. 8va)

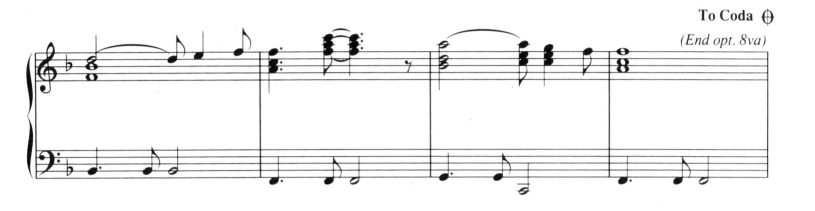

D.S. al Coda

CODA

f

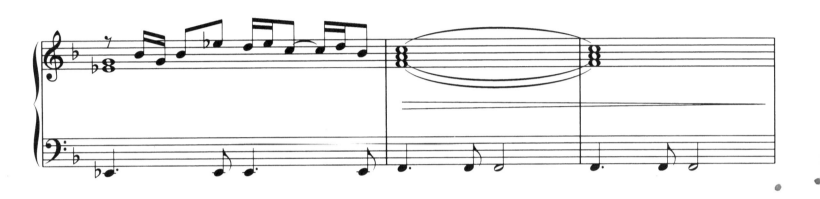

MOONLIGHT SONATA OP.27, NO.2

Ludwig van Beethoven

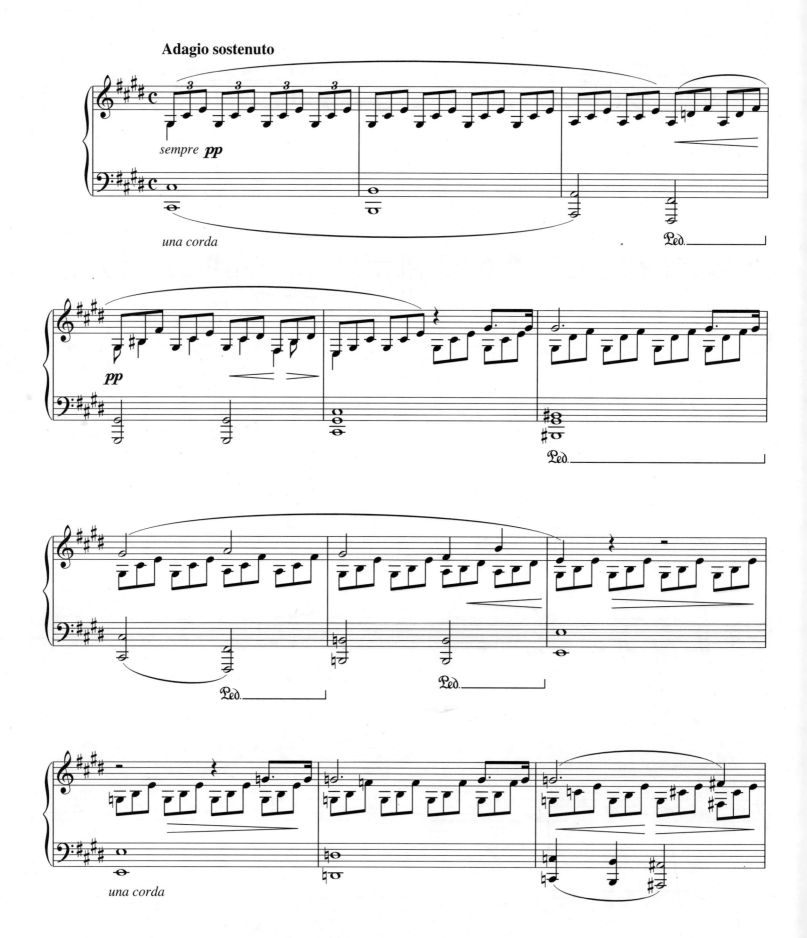

PIANO SONATA IN D MAJOR
(ADAGIO)

Wolfgang Amadeus Mozart

PIANO CONCERTO NO.2
(ADAGIO SOSTENUTO)

Sergei Rachmaninov

PIANO SONATA IN F MINOR OP.57, NO.23
(2ND MOVEMENT)

Ludwig Van Beethoven

Andante con moto

PRELUDE IN C

Johann Sebastian Bach

PRELUDE IN E MINOR OP.28, NO.4

Frédéric Chopin

a tempo

SERENADE FOR STRINGS IN C MAJOR OP.48
(WALTZ)

Pyotr Ilyich Tchaikovsky

THE SWAN
(FROM 'THE CARNIVAL OF THE ANIMALS')

Camille Saint-Saëns

Andantino grazioso ♩ = 80

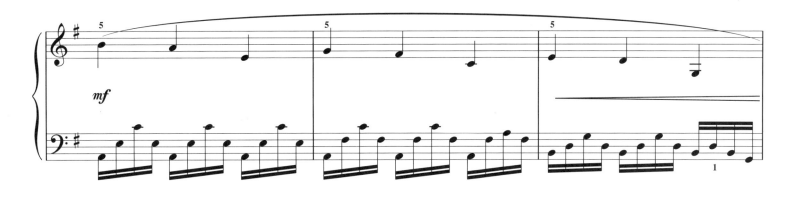

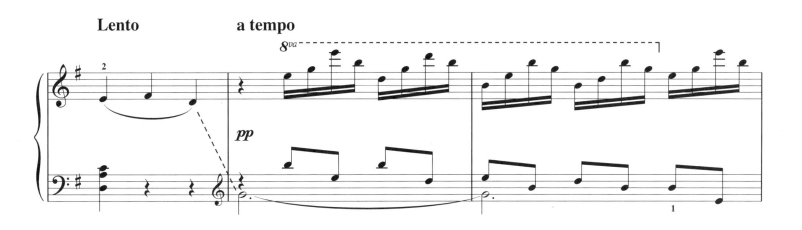

STRING QUARTET NO.2 IN D MAJOR
(THEME)

Alexander Borodin

Andante ♩ = 60

cantabile ed espressivo

cantabile ed espresso

TRÄUMEREI OP.15, NO.7

Robert Schumann

VOCALISE

Sergei Rachmaninov

Lentamente e molto cantabile ♪ = 84

Poco più animato

Poco più mosso

VIOLIN CONCERTO IN E MINOR OP.64
(ANDANTE)

Felix Mendelssohn

Andante ♪ = 96

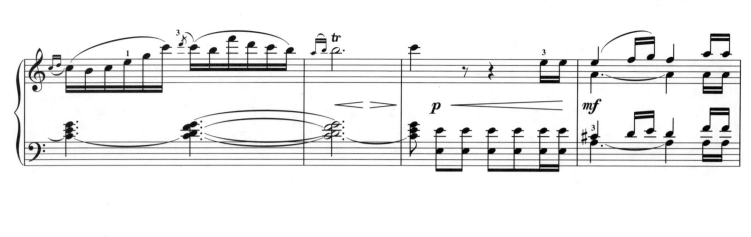